The Silly Little Book

of

JOKES

ABOUT GIRLS

The Silly Little Book
of

JOKES ABOUT
GIRLS

This is a Parragon Book

This edition published in 2001

Parragon
Queen Street House
4 Queen Street
Bath BA1 1HE, UK

Produced by Magpie Books, an imprint of
Robinson Publishing Ltd, London

ISBN 0-75253-694-X

A copy of the British Library Cataloguing-in-Publication Data
is available from the British Library

Printed and bound in Singapore

Contents

Introduction

Whether you've got a face like a million dollars (green and wrinkly), your favorite band is "The Lice Girls," or your name is Annette Curtain, this book is an education! For the girls amongst us, there's nothing better than having a laugh at your own funny little habits (honest)! For the rest of us, there's a treat in store. All you need is a girl to try them out on . . .

Jokes
about Girls

What do you call a girl with a frog on her head?
Lily.

How does a witch doctor ask a girl to dance?
"Voodoo like to dance with me?"

What did one maggot say to another?
"What's a nice girl like you doing in a joint like this?"

"Please, Miss!" said a little girl at kindergarten. "We're going to play elephants and circuses, do you want to join in?"

"I'd love to," said the teacher. "What do you want me to do?"

"You can be the lady that feeds us peanuts!"

Small girl: I'd buy that dog, but his legs are too short.

Clerk: Too short? Why, all four of them touch the floor.

Why did the wizard turn the
naughty girl into a mouse?
Because she ratted on him.

What kind of girl does a mummy
take on a date?
Any old girl he can dig up.

What do ghosts say when a girl
footballer is sent off?
Ban-she, ban-she!

First monster: That pretty girl over there just rolled her eyes at me.
Second monster: Well you'd better roll them back to her, she might need them.

What happened to the girl who wore a mouse costume to her halloween party?
The cat ate her.

Who is a vampire likely to fall in love with?
The girl necks door.

What happened when the girl dressed as a spoon left the Halloween party?
No one moved. They couldn't stir without her.

First witch: My, hasn't your little girl grown?
Second witch: Yes, she's certainly gruesome.

What do you call a top pop group made up of nits?
The Lice Girls.

Who was that I saw you with last
night?
It was a girl from the school.
Teacher?
Didn't have to!

Two girls were having their packed
lunch in the school yard. One had
an apple and the other said,
"Watch out for worms won't you!"
The first one replied, "Why should
I? They can watch out for
themselves."

"What were you before you came to school, girls?" asked the teacher, hoping that someone would say babies.

She was disappointed when all the girls cried out, "Happy!"

Teacher: I'd like you to be very quiet today, girls. I've got a dreadful headache.

Mary: Please, Miss! Why don't you do what Mom does when she has a headache?

Teacher: What's that?

Mary: She sends us out to play.

"I'm very sad to announce this morning, girls, that Miss Jones has decided to retire," said the principal at morning assembly. "Now we will all stand and sing this morning's hymn . . . Now Thank We All Our God."

How does a blonde kill a fish? She drowns it.

Jane: Do you like me?
Wayne: As girls go, you're fine. And the sooner you go the better!

When a blonde goes to London on a plane, how can you steal her window seat?
Tell her the seats that are going to London are all in the middle row.

"Now remember, girls," said the science teacher. "You can tell a tree's age by counting the rings in a cross section. One ring for each year."
Alice went home from school and found a chocolate roll on the table.
"I'm not eating that, Mum," she said. "It's five years old."

Two little girls at a very posh school were talking to each other.

"I told the chauffeur to take his peaked cap off in case the other girls here thought I was a snob," said the first.

"How strange," said the second, "I told mine to keep his on in case anyone thought he was my father."

Some girls who are the picture of health are just painted that way.

Two girls were talking in the corridor. "That boy over there is getting on my nerves," said Clarrie.

"But he's not even looking at you," replied Clara.

"That's what's getting on my nerves," retorted Clarrie.

Did you hear about the teacher who was trying to instil good table manners in her girls? She told them, "A well-mannered girl never crumbles her bread or rolls in her soup."

Two boys were watching TV when the fabulous face and figure of Demi Moore appeared on the screen. "If I ever stop hating girls," said one to the other, "I think I'll stop hating her first."

A little girl was next in line. "My name's Curtain," she said.
"I hope your first name's not Annette?"
"No. It's Velvet."

On the first day at school the girls were sizing each other up and boasting, trying to make good impressions on each other.

"I come from a one-parent family," said one little girl proudly.

"That's nothing. Both my parents remarried after they got divorced. I come from a four-parent family."

"The girl beside me in math is very clever," said Alec to his mother. "She's got enough brains for two."

"Perhaps you'd better think of marriage," replied Mom.

"Ann!" the teacher shouted one day at the girl who had been daydreaming out the window. "If India has the world's second largest population, oranges are 50 cents for six and it costs $3 for a day return to Austin, how old am I?"

"Thirty-two!"

"Why did you say that?"

"Well, my brother's sixteen and he's half mad!"

"You never get anything right," complained the teacher. "What kind of job do you think you'll get when you leave school?"
"Well I want to be the weather girl on TV."

As he was walking along the street the minister saw a little girl trying to reach a high door knocker. Anxious to help, he went over to her. "Let me do it, dear," he said, rapping the knocker vigorously. "Great!" said the girl. "Now run like hell."

A fat girl went into a cafe and ordered two slices of apple pie with four scoops of ice cream covered with lashings of raspberry sauce and piles of chopped nuts.

"Would you like a cherry on the top?" asked the waitress.

"No, thanks," said the girl, "I'm on a diet."

Boy Monster: You've got a face like a million dollars.

Girl Monster: Have I really?

Boy Monster: Yes – it's green and wrinkly.

Did you hear about the girl
monster who wasn't pretty and
wasn't ugly?
She was pretty ugly.

Did you hear about the Eskimo
teacher who was reciting Little
Jack Horner to her class of five-
year-olds? She'd got as far as
"Little Jack Horner sat in a corner"
when one little girl put up her hand
and said, "Please, Miss, what's a
corner?"

What did one magician say to another?
Who was that girl I sawed you with last night?

First cannibal: Who was that girl I saw you with last night?
Second cannibal: That was no girl, that was my supper.

What did the Eskimo schoolboy say to the Eskimo schoolgirl?
What's an ice girl like you doing in a place like this?

She's the kind of girl that boys look at twice – they can't believe it the first time.

Did you hear about the girl who got engaged to a chap and then found out he had a wooden leg? She broke it off, of course . . .

Why didn't the female frog lay eggs?
Because her husband spawned her affections.

Father: I want to take my girl out of this terrible math class.

Teacher: But she's top of the class.

Father: That's why I think it must be a terrible class.

$$\begin{array}{r} 3467 \\ + 9876 \\ \hline 13343 \end{array}$$

After a visit to the circus, Geoff and Don were discussing the thrills and marvels they had seen.

"I didn't think much of the knife-thrower, did you?" said Geoff.

"I thought he was great!" enthused Don.

"Well I didn't," said Geoff. "He kept chucking those knives at that soppy girl but he didn't hit her once."

"What do you do?" a young man asked the beautiful girl he was dancing with.

"I'm a nurse."

"I wish I could be ill and let you nurse me," he whispered in her ear.

"That would be miraculous. I work on the maternity ward."

Handsome Harry: Every time I walk past a girl she sighs.

Wisecracking William: With relief!

"The walls in my apartment are very thin," a young girl complained to her friend.
"You mean you can hear everything that's going on next door?"
"Not just that: when they peel onions I start to cry!"

Why was the Egyptian girl worried?
'Cos her Daddy was a mummy.

That girl looks like Helen Black.
She looks even worse in white.

Belinda: James told me last night that he'd met the most beautiful girl in the world.
Barbara: Oh, dear, I'm so sorry. I thought he was going to marry you.

What is a myth?
A female moth.

What do young female monsters do at parties?
They go around looking for edible bachelors.

This girl wanted to marry a ghost.
I can't think what possessed her.

Why did the small werewolf bite
the girl's ankle?
Because he couldn't reach any
higher.

A girl walked into a pet shop and
said, "I'd like a frog for my
brother."
"Sorry," said the shopkeeper, "We
don't do part exchange."

The garbage men were just about
to leave the street when a girl
came running out of the house
carrying some cardboard boxes.
"Am I too late for the garbage?"
she called.
"No," replied one of the men,
"Jump right in!"

Did you hear about the girl who
was so keen on road safety that
she always wore white at night?
Last winter she was knocked down
by a snow plow.

An irate girl burst into the baker's shop and said: "I sent my brother in for two pounds of cookies this morning but when I weighed them there was only one pound. I suggest you check your scales." The baker replied, "My dear, I suggest you weigh your brother."

What nickname did the police give to the new blonde woman police officer?
A fair cop.

"I beg your pardon," said the man, returning to his seat in the theater, "but did I step on your toe as I went out?"

"You certainly did," the girl replied.

"Oh good," said the man, "that means I'm in the right row."

Roger was in a very full bus when a fat girl opposite said, "If you were a gentleman, you'd stand up and let someone else sit down."

"And if you were a lady," replied Roger, "you'd stand up and let four people sit down."

First girl: Whenever I'm down in the dumps I buy myself a new hat.
Second girl: Oh, so that's where you get them.

How do you poison a girl with a pair of scissors?
Give her arseanick!

"Five dollars for one question!" said the girl to the fortuneteller.
"That's very expensive, isn't it?"
"Next!"

Teacher: Who was the first woman on earth?
Angela: I don't know, Sir.
Teacher: Come on, Angela, it has something to do with an apple.
Angela: Granny Smith?

"Those currant buns you sold me yesterday had three cockroaches in them," a girl complained over the phone to a baker.
"Sorry about that," said the baker. "If you bring the cockroaches back I'll give you the three currants I owe you."

Why did the girl take a load of hay to bed?
To feed her nightmare.

A girl just back from the United States was telling her friends about the trip. "When my brother first saw the Grand Canyon, his face dropped a mile," she said. "Why, was he disappointed with the view?"

"No, he fell over the edge."

Sisters

Why did your sister go to night school?
Because she wanted to learn to read in the dark.

Lucy: If you eat any more ice cream, you'll burst.
Lindy: OK. Pass the ice cream and duck.

Mother: Jared, get your little sister's hat out of that puddle.
Jared: I can't, Mom, she's got it strapped too tight under her chin.

Janet: What's the difference between a cake and a school bus?
Jill: I don't know.
Janet: I'm glad I didn't send you to pick up my birthday cake.

Karen: Have you noticed that Daddy is getting taller?
Sharon: No, why?
Karen: His head is sticking though his hair.

My sister is so dumb she thinks that a buttress is a female goat.

Danny: What are you doing, Sis?
Marilyn: Writing my cousin a letter.
Danny: Why are you writing so slow?
Marilyn: Because he can't read very fast.

Boy: Dad, dad, come out. My sister's fighting this ten foot gargoyle with three heads.
Dad: No, I'm not coming out. She's going to have to learn to look after herself.

Sandra and Simon were arguing furiously over the breakfast table.
"Oh, you're stupid!" shouted Simon.
"Simon!" said their father, "that's quite enough of that! Now say you're sorry."
"All right," said Simon. "Sandra, I'm sorry you're stupid."

What was the cannibal called who ate his father's sister?
An aunt-eater.

Boy: My sister's the school swot.
Girl: Does she do well in exams?
Boy: No, but she kills a lot of flies.

Witch: Why have you stopped
playing cards with my sister?
Wizard: Well would you play with
someone who cheats all the time,
is a poor loser and keeps tearing
up the cards?
Witch: No I wouldn't.
Wizard: No, well nor will she.

Did you hear about my sister? She saw a moose's head hanging on a wall and went into the next room to see the rest of it.

Why did your sister put a chicken in a tub of hot water?
Because she wanted the chicken to lay hard-boiled eggs.

Big brother: That planet up there is Mars.
Little sister: Then that other one must be Pa's.

Why did your sister cut a hole in her new umbrella?
Because she wanted to be able to tell when it stopped raining.

Father: Why did you put a toad in your sister's bed?
Son: I couldn't find a spider.

Did you hear about the sister who wrote herself a letter and forgot to sign it, and when it arrived she didn't know who it was from?

Did you hear about the boy who saw a witch riding on a broomstick? He said, "What are you doing on that?"
She replied, "My sister's got the vacuum cleaner."

Why did your sister shoot the alarm clock?
Because she felt like killing time.

Witch: Doctor, Doctor, my sister here keeps thinking she's invisible.
Doctor: Which sister?

Why did your sister separate the
thread from the needle?
Because the needle had
something in its eye.

Why did your sister wear a wet
shirt all day?
Because the label said, "Wash and
Wear."

Why did your sister spend two
weeks in a revolving door?
Because she was looking for the
doorknob.

Witch: Doctor, Doctor, my sisters think I'm mad because I like peas.
Doctor: There's nothing wrong with that, I like peas too.
Witch: Oh good, come back to my hovel and I'll show you my collection.

A little demon came home from school one day and said to his mother, "I hate my sister's guts." "All right," said his mother, "I won't put them in your sandwiches again."

My sister thinks that a juggernaut is an empty beer mug.

"What's your father's occupation?" asked the school secretary on the first day of the new term.
"He's a conjurer, Miss," said the new girl.
"How interesting. What's his favorite trick?"
"He saws people in half."
"Golly! Now next question. Any brothers and sisters?"
"One half brother and two half sisters."

Why was the boy unhappy to win the prize for the best costume at the Halloween party?
Because he just came by to pick up his little sister.

My sister is so dim she thinks that a cartoon is a song you sing in a car.

My sister is so stupid she thinks that aroma is someone who travels a lot.

First Vampire: I don't think much of your sister's neck.

Second Vampire: Never mind – eat the vegetables instead.

Teacher: What's this a picture of?

Class: Don't know, miss.

Teacher: It's a kangaroo.

Class: What's a kangaroo, miss?

Teacher: A kangaroo is a native of Australia.

Smallest boy: Wow, my sister's married one of them!

Did you hear about the time
Eddy's sister tried to make a
birthday cake?
The candles melted in the oven.

"Why is your son crying?" the
doctor asked a young woman in his
surgery.
"He has four baked beans stuck
up his nose."
"And why is his little sister
screaming?"
"She wants the rest of her lunch
back."

Why did your sister jump out the window?
Because she wanted to try out her new spring suit!

Susannah was watching her big sister covering her face with cream. "What's that for?" she asked.
"To make me beautiful," came the reply.
Susannah then watched in silence as she wiped her face clean.
"Doesn't work, does it?" was the young sister's comment.

Doctor! Doctor! My sister thinks she's an elevator.
Tell her to come in.
I can't. She doesn't stop at this floor.

Alfie was listening to his sister practice her singing. "Sis," he said, "I wish you'd sing Christmas carols."
"That's nice of you, Alfie," she replied. "Why?"
"Then I'd only have to hear you once a year!"

Mary: Do you think my sister's pretty?
Gary: Well, let's just say if you pulled her pigtail she'd probably say "Oink, oink"!

Why was your sister fired from her job as an elevator operator?
Because she couldn't remember the route.

Little brother: Look, sis, I've got a deck of cards.
Big sister: Big deal!

Why did your sister refuse the gift of a Japanese car?
Because she'd never be able to learn the language!

Did you hear about the girl that got her brother a birthday cake, but could not figure out how to get the cake in the typewriter to write "Happy Birthday?"

Why did your sister plant birdseed?
Because she wanted to raise canaries.

Why did your sister ask your father to sit in the refrigerator?
Because she wanted ice-cold pop!

Why does your sister wear a life jacket to bed?
Because she sleeps on a water bed!

Come here, you greedy wretch. I'll teach you to eat all your sister's birthday chocs.
It's all right, Dad, I know how.

You might find my sister a bit dull until you get to know her. When you do you'll discover she's a real bore!

Jane: Have you noticed that your mother smells a bit funny these days?

Wayne: No. Why?

Jane: Well your sister told me she was giving her a bottle of toilet water for her birthday.

Jim: My sister wants to be an actress.

Tim: Is she pretty?

Jim: Well, put it this way, she'd be perfect on radio.

Gill: Your sister uses too much makeup.

Jen: Do you think so?

Gill: Yes. It's so thick that if you tell her a joke, five minutes after she's stopped laughing her face is still smiling!

Michael: It's hard for my sister to eat.

Maureen: Why?

Michael: She can't bear to stop talking.

Your sister's boyfriend certainly has staying power. In fact, he never leaves.

Do you like my new baby sister?
The stork brought her.
Hmm, it looks as if the stork dropped her on her head.

Why did your sister tiptoe past the medicine cabinet?
Because she didn't want to wake the sleeping pills.

My sister went on a crash diet.
Is that why she looks a wreck?

My sister fell in love at second
sight. When she first met him she
didn't know how rich he was.

Why did your sister refuse to
accept tickets for a door prize?
Because she already had a door!

Brother: How do you top a car?
Sister: Tep on the brake, tupid.

Brother: If you broke your arm in two places, what would you do?
Sister: I wouldn't go back to those two places.

Why does your sister jump up and down before taking her medicine?
Because the label said, "Shake well before using."

Why did your sister give cough syrup to the pony?
Because someone told her it was a little horse.

Why does your sister have yeast
and shoe polish for breakfast?
Because she wants to rise and
shine!

Brother: Did you just take a
shower?
Sister: Why, is one missing?

Why did your sister keep running
around her bed?
Because she was trying to catch
up with her sleep.

Brother: Why is that dog staring at me like that?
Sister: Don't mind him. He's just mad 'cos you're eating out of his dish!

Why did your sister put her socks on inside out?
Because there was a hole on the outside.

Brother: What two things can you never eat for breakfast?
Sister: Lunch and dinner.

Why did your sister take a bicycle to bed?
Because she didn't want to walk in her sleep.

Brother: What happened to you?
Sister: I fell while I was riding.
Brother: Horseback?
Sister: I don't know. I'll find out when I get back to the barn!

Why does your sister pick up soap bubbles and put them to her ear?
Because she likes soap operas.

Sister: Why are you putting the saddle on backward?
Brother: How do you know which way I'm going?

Why did your sister pitch the tent on top of the stove?
Because she wanted a home on the range!

Brother: Did you put the cat out?
Sister: Why, is it on fire?

Why does your sister not like
peanuts?
Has anyone ever seen a skinny
elephant?

Brother: What kind of sharks never
eat women?
Sister: Man-eating sharks.

Why did your sister feed money to
her cow?
Because she wanted to get rich
milk.

Why couldn't your sister spell
Mississippi when the teacher
asked her?
Because she didn't know if she
meant the river or the state!

Sister: What goes up but never
comes down?
Brother: Your age!

Girlfriends

What did the wizard say to his
witch girlfriend?
Hello gore-juice!

What did the zombie's friend say
when he introduced him to his
girlfriend?
Good grief! Where did you dig her
up from?

What does a zombie say when he
gets a letter from his girlfriend?
It's a dead-letter day.

Two teenage boys were talking in the classroom. One said, "I took my girlfriend to see 'The Bride of Dracula' last night."

"Oh yeah," said the other, "what was she like?"

"Well she was about six foot six, white as a ghost and she had big red staring eyes and fangs."

The other said, "Yes, but what was 'The Bride of Dracula' like?"

What did the skeleton say to his girlfriend?

I love every bone in your body.

Why did the vampire's girlfriend break up with him?
Because he had such a powerful crush on her.

When my girlfriend goes out riding, she looks like part of the horse. When she dismounts, she still looks like part of the horse.

Flash Harry gave his girlfriend a mink stole for her birthday. Well, it may not have been mink, but it's fairly certain it was stole.

One day Tony's girlfriend wrote to him to say their friendship was off and could she have her photograph back? Tony sent her a pile of pictures of different girls with the message: I can't remember what you look like. Could you please take out your photo and return the rest.

My girlfriend talks so much that when she goes on vacation, she has to spread suntan lotion on her tongue.

My girlfriend thinks I'm a great wit. Well, she's half right.

Simon: My girlfriend and I fell out last night. She wanted to go and watch ice-skating, but I wanted to go to the football match.
Peter: What was the ice-skating like?

What did the undertaker say to his girlfriend?
Em-balmy about you.

I can't understand why people say my girlfriend's legs look like matchsticks. They do look like sticks – but they certainly don't match.

Ben's new girlfriend uses such greasy lipstick that he has to sprinkle his face with sand to get a better grip.

Every time I take my girlfriend out for a meal she eats her head off. She looks better that way.

71

Anne: Ugh! The water in my glass is cloudy.

Dan, trying to impress his new girlfriend: It's all right, it's just the glass that hasn't been washed.

My girlfriend is a beautiful redhead – no hair, just a red head.

My girlfriend has a slight impediment in her speech. Every so often, she has to stop to breathe.

First cannibal: My girlfriend's a tough old bird.

Second cannibal: You should have left her in the oven for another half an hour.

"What's your new perfume called?" a young man asked his girlfriend.

"High Heaven," she replied.

"I asked what it was called, not what it smells to!"

James: I call my girlfriend Peach.
John: Because she's beautiful?
James: No, because she's got a heart of stone!

A monster walked into a store selling dress fabrics and said, "I'd like six yards of pink satan for my girlfriend."

"It's satin, sir, not satan," said the clerk. "Satan is something that looks like the devil."

"Oh," said the monster, "you know my girlfriend?"

When Wally Witherspoon proposed to his girlfriend she said, "I love the simple things in life, Wally, but I don't want one of them for a husband."

I got a gold watch for my
girlfriend.
I wish I could make a trade like
that!

Why did the jelly fish's girlfriend
leave him?
He stung her into action.

What did the executioner say to
his girlfriend? Only thirty chopping
days to Christmas.

First man: My girlfriend eats like a bird.

Second man: You mean she hardly eats a thing?

First man: No, she eats slugs and worms.

Beautician: Did that mud pack I gave you for your girlfriend improve her appearance?

Man: It did for a while – then it fell off.

Waiter, waiter! What's this creepy crawly thing doing on my girlfriend's shoulder?
I don't know – friendly little thing, isn't he?

Two men were having a drink together. One said, "I'd rather date a vampire than my girlfriend."
"Why's that?" asked the other.
He replied, "Because she's always trying to bite my head off."

Doctor, Doctor, my girlfriend thinks she's a duck.
You better bring her in to see me straight away.
I can't do that – she's already flown south for the winter.

Two cannibals were having lunch. "Your girlfriend makes a great soup," said one to the other. "Yes!" agreed the first. "But I'm going to miss her terribly."

A man who forgets his girlfriend's birthday is certain to get something to remember her by.

Freddie had persuaded Amanda to marry him, and was formally asking her father for his permission. "Sir," he said, "I would like to have your daughter for my wife."

"Why can't she get one of her own?" asked Amanda's father.

Do you think, Professor, that my
girlfriend should take up the piano
as a career?
No, I think she should put down
the lid as a favor.

Doctor Sawbones speaking.
Oh, doctor, my girlfriend's just
dislocated her jaw. Can you come
over in, say, three or four weeks'
time?

"It's a pity you've gone on hunger strike," said the convict's girlfriend on visiting day. "Why?"
"I've put a file in your cake."

My girlfriend says that if I don't give up golf she'll leave me.
Say, that's tough, old man.
Yeah, I'm going to miss her.

My brother's looking for a girlfriend. Trouble is, he can't find a girl who loves him as much as he loves himself.

Darling Daughter

"What's wrong, Jeanie?" asked her father.

"I lost my puppy," sobbed Jeanie.

"Don't cry," said the concerned father. "We'll get your dog back. We'll put an ad in the paper."

"That won't do any good," wailed Jeanie. "The dog can't read!"

Annie: May I have a quarter for the crying man outside?

Mother: What crying man?

Annie: The one that's crying, "Ice cream! Ice cream!"

Mother, I just took a splinter out of
my hand with a pin.
A pin! Don't you know that's
dangerous?
Oh no, Mother, I used a safety pin.

Father: Where's this morning's
newspaper?
Daughter: I wrapped the garbage
in it and threw it out.
Father: But I wanted to see it!
Daughter: There wasn't much to
see. Only an apple core, two steak
bones and some coffee grounds.

Kitty kept pestering her parents to buy a video, but they said they couldn't afford one. So one day Kitty came home clutching a package containing a brand-new video.

"Wherever did you get the money to pay for that?" asked her father suspiciously.

"It's all right, Dad," replied Kitty, "I traded the TV in for it."

What did Dracula call his daughter?
Bloody Mary.

Karen wanted to be a doctor when she grew up. She bandaged and cared for her dolls, and often went on imaginary sick calls to someone in the neighborhood.

One day she ran out on such a call, forgetting to close the door behind her. When her mother insisted she come back and shut it, Karen did so and raced away.

That evening her mother asked, "How is the patient getting along?"

"She died," said Karen. "Died while I was closing that door!"

Angie was late for school. "Angie!" roared her mother. "Have you got your socks on yet?"

"Yes, Mom," replied Angie. "All except one."

Glenn: Kathy, Mom says to run across the street and see how old Mrs Planter is.

Kathy: OK.

Mom (to Kathy): Well, what did she say?

Kathy: She says it's none of your business how old she is.

Dad: Katie, why is your January
report card so bad?
Katie: You know how it is, Dad.
Things are always marked down
after Christmas.

Nikki: I bet I can make you say
"black." What are the colors of the
flag?
Mother: Red, white and blue.
Nikki: I told you I could make you
say "black."
Mother: I didn't say "black."

89

Mrs Johnston, your daughter
would be a fine dancer except for
two things.
What are they?
Her feet!

It was getting close to Christmas and the mother asked her ten-year-old daughter what she would like as a gift. "A mirror, Mommy," came the reply.

"My goodness. Why?"

"Because," sighed the daughter, "I'm getting too big to make up in the doorknob."

"Mom," Jenny yelled from the kitchen, "you know that dish you were always worried I'd break?"

"Yes, dear. What about it?"

"Well, your worries are over."

Father: Doctor, come quick! My girl just swallowed our pocket-size TV!
Doctor: I'll be right over. What are you doing in the meantime?
Father: I don't know. I guess we'll have to listen to the radio.

Mother: Don't be selfish. Let your sister use the sled half the time.
Daughter: I do, Mom. I use it going down the hill, and she gets to use it coming up.

Little Jackie fell off her bicycle
and cut her knee. Her mother
bathed and dressed the wound,
and then gave the girl a pill to
soothe her.
After she swallowed it, Jackie
asked, "How will the pill know
which leg to go down?"

Amy: I'm so glad I'm not a bird.
Father: Why?
Amy: I can't fly!

Mother: Sara, haven't you finished filling the salt shaker yet?

Sara: Not yet, Mom. It's awful hard to get the salt through those little holes!

Teacher: Your daughter's only five and she can spell her name backward? Why, that is remarkable.

Mother: Yes, we're very proud of her.

Teacher: And what is your daughter's name?

Mother: Anna.

Mary: Dad, that dentist wasn't painless like he advertised.
Father: Did he hurt you, Mary?
Mary: No, but he sure did scream when I bit his finger!

Mom: Jenny, how can you practice your trumpet and listen to the radio at the same time?
Jenny: I have two ears.

School Doctor to Parent: I'm afraid your daughter needs glasses.
Parent: How can you tell?
School Doctor: By the way she came in through the window.

Mary arrived home from school covered in spots. "Whatever's the matter?" asked her mother.
"I don't know," replied Mary, "but the teacher thinks I may have caught decimals."

Mother: Did you get a good place in the geography test?
Daughter: Yes, Mom, I sat next to the cleverest kid in the class.

Mother: I told you not to eat cake before supper.
Daughter: But, Mom, it's part of my homework. "If you take an eighth of a cake from a whole cake, how much is left?"

Mother: What do you mean, the school must be haunted?
Daughter: Well, the principal kept going on about the school spirit.

"But she's so young to get married," sobbed Diana's mother. "Only seventeen!"
"Try not to cry about it," said her husband soothingly. "Think of it not as losing a daughter but as gaining a bathroom."

Mrs Jones and her little daughter Karen were outside the church watching all the comings and goings of a wedding. After all the excitement was over Karen said to her mother, "Why did the bride change her mind, Mommy?"

"How do you mean, change her mind?" asked Mrs Jones.

"Well," said Karen, "she went into the church with one man and came out with another."

Mom: Jackie, go outside and play with your whistle. Your father can't read his paper.
Jackie: Wow, I'm only eight, and I can read it!

"I'm very worried about my little girl's nail-biting habit," a woman said to her doctor.
"Nail biting is very common in youngsters," said the doctor.
"What! Six-inch rusty ones?"

Mother: Do you know a girl named Jenny Simon?
Daughter: Yes, she sleeps next to me in math.

Jane's father decided to take all the family out to a restaurant for a meal. As he'd spent quite a lot of money on the meal he said to the waiter, "Could I have a bag to take the leftovers home for the dog?" "Gosh!" exclaimed Jane, "Are we getting a dog?"

Mother to Friend: Karen's so imaginative! I asked her what the "F" meant on her report, and she said "Fantastic."

Mom: Sue, there were two chocolate cakes in the larder yesterday, and now there's only one. Why?
Sue: I don't know. It must have been so dark I didn't see the other one.

Father: Jennifer, I've had a letter from your teacher. It seems you've been neglecting your appearance.
Jennifer: Dad?
Father: He says you haven't appeared in school all week.

Mary's class was taken to the Natural History Museum. "Did you enjoy yourself?" asked her mother when she got home.
"Oh yes," replied Mary. "But it was funny going to a dead zoo."

Janet came home from school and asked her mother if the aerosol spray in the kitchen was hair lacquer. "No," said Mom, "it's glue."

"I thought so," said Janet. "I wondered why I couldn't get my beret off today."

She Said That, Did She?

Girl: How much is a soft drink?
Waitress: Fifty cents.
Girl: How much is a refill?
Waitress: The first is free.
Girl: Well then, I'll have a refill.

The second grader was in bed with a cold and a high temperature. "How high is it, Doctor?" she wanted to know.
"One hundred and three," said the doctor.
"What is the world record?"

A girl rushed into the doctor's office and said, "Doctor, I think I'm going crazy. I have a carrot growing out of my left ear."

"So you have," said the amazed doctor. "How can such a thing happen?"

"I can't understand it," said the bewildered girl. "I planted a cabbage."

Cindy: My kitten likes to drink lemonade.

Kim: Boy, he sure must be a sourpuss.

Trevor: That's a cool pair of stockings you have on, Jill. One red and one green.

Jill: Yes, and I have another pair just like it at home.

"Can you lend me $1,000?"

"I only have $800."

"That's all right. You can owe me the other $200."

Brother: Where was Solomon's temple?

Sister: On either side of his head.

Mom: How did you do in the grammar test?
Kate: Great, Mom. I only made one mistake and I seen it as soon as I done it.

Little Susie stood in a department store near the escalator, watching the moving handrail.
"Something wrong, little girl?" inquired the security guard.
"Nope," replied Susie, "just waiting for my chewing gum to come back."

John: I'm going to cross a galaxy
with a frog.
Sharon: You'd better not. You'll be
sorry.
John: Why?
Sharon: Don't you know what you'll
get?
John: No. What?
Sharon: Star warts.

Why did you refuse to marry
Richard, Tessa?
'Cos he said he would die if I
didn't and I'm just curious.

Mandy was applying for a summer job.

"How old are you?" asked the owner of the store.

"I'm twelve years old, Sir," answered Mandy.

"And what do you expect to be when you grow up?"

"Twenty-one, Sir."

Science Teacher: Can you tell me one substance that conducts electricity, Jane?

Jane: Why, er . . .

Science Teacher: Wire is correct.

Why are you crying, Janie?
Because my new tennis shoes hurt.
That's because you put them on the wrong feet.
Well, they're the only feet I have.

Suresh: Whatever will Clive do when he leaves school? I can't see him being bright enough to get a job.
Sandra: He could always be a ventriloquist's dummy.

Little Sheila's mother was on the telephone to the girl's dentist. "I don't understand it," she complained, "I thought her treatment would only cost me $20, but you've charged me $80."

"It is usually $20, ma'am," agreed the dentist, "but Sheila yelled so loudly that three of my other patients ran away!"

Teacher: Didn't you know the bell had gone?
Silly Sue: I didn't take it, Miss.

"Mary," said her teacher. "You can't bring that lamb into school. What about the smell?"

"Oh, that's all right, Miss," replied Mary. "It'll soon get used to it."

Why did Silly Sue throw her guitar
away?
Because it had a hole in the
middle.

Jennifer: Are you coming to my
party?
Sandra: No, I ain't.
Jennifer: Now, you know what Miss
told us. Not ain't. It's I am not
coming, he is not coming, she is
not coming, they are not coming.
Sandra: Blimey, ain't nobody
coming?

Visitor: You're very quiet, Jennifer.
Jennifer: Well, my mom gave me a dollar not to say anything about your red nose.

A garbage man was walking along whistling while balancing a garbage can on his head and one on each shoulder.

"How do you manage to do that?" asked Jane.

"It's easy," replied the garbage man. "Just put your lips together and blow."

Biology Teacher: What kinds of
birds do we get in captivity?
Janet: Jail birds, Miss!

Mother: Did you enjoy the school
outing, dear?
Jane: Yes. And we're going again
tomorrow.
Mother: Really? Why's that?
Jane: To try and find the kids we
left behind.

"Did you thank Mrs Pillbeam for teaching you today?" Janie's mom asked her when she came home from school.

"No I didn't. Mary in front of me did and Mrs Pillbeam said 'Don't mention it', so I didn't."

Teacher: Are you good at arithmetic?

Mary: Well, yes and no.

Teacher: What do you mean, yes and no?

Mary: Yes, I'm no good at arithmetic.

Grandma: You've left all your crusts, Mary. When I was your age I ate every one.

Mary: Do you still like crusts, Grandma?

Grandma: Yes, I do.

Mary: Well, you can have mine.

Jane: Do you ever do any gardening?

Wayne: Not often. Why?

Jane: You look as if you could do with some remedial weeding.

Mary: I've a soft spot for you.
Harry: Really?
Mary: Yes, in the middle of a bog!

Mary: There's no point in telling you a joke with a double meaning.
Cary: Why not?
Mary: You wouldn't get either of them.

Darren: I'm so tired I feel like an old sock.
Sharon: I thought there was a funny smell in here!

A rather stern aunt had been staying with Sharon's parents, and one day she said to the little girl, "Well, Sharon, I'm going home tomorrow. Are you sorry?"
"Oh yes, Auntie," replied Sharon, "I thought you were going today."

Gemma: I've been told I look just like an Italian dish.
Emma: You do.
Gemma: Really? Sophia Loren? Gina Lollobrigida?
Emma: No, spaghetti bolognese.

Sharon: I'm so homesick.
Sheila: But this is your home!
Sharon: I know, and I'm sick of it!

"What shall we play today?" said
Theresa to her best friend Emma.
"Let's play schools," said Emma.
"OK!" said Theresa. "But I'm
going to be absent."

Cookery teacher: Helen, what are
the best things to put in a fruit
cake?
Helen: Teeth!

Emma: I'd like to say something nice about you as it's your birthday.

Gemma: Why don't you?

Emma: Because I can't think of a single thing to say!

Helen: Mom, do you know what I'm going to give you for your birthday?

Mom: No, dear, what?

Helen: A nice teapot.

Mom: But I've got a nice teapot.

Helen: No you haven't. I've just dropped it!

The Love Bug

What happened when a female monster fell in love with a grand piano?
She said, "Darling, you've got lovely teeth."

Why did the witch go to the psychiatrist?
Because she thought everybody loved her.

Witch: When I'm old and ugly will you still love me.
Wizard: I do, don't I?

A lady put a lonely hearts ad in the paper and had a reply which said, "I would love to meet you but I have to tell you that I am eight feet tall, covered in matted fur, with large fangs and slobbering lips. If you still want to meet me then I'll be under the clock in the market square at six o'clock next Saturday."

The lady replied, "I would be interested in meeting you but please will you wear a red carnation and carry a rolled-up copy of The New York Times so that I can recognize you?"

What happened when the young
wizard met the young witch?
It was love at first fright.

Did you hear about the vampire
who died of a broken heart?
He had loved in vein.

What did one centipede say to
another?
You've got a lovely pair of legs, pair
of legs, pair of legs . . .

Julie had broken off her
engagement. Her friend asked
her what had happened. "I
thought it was love at first sight,"
said Julie. "It was, but it was the
second and third sights that
changed my mind."

What did the two acrobats say
when they got married?
We're head over heels in love!

Harry was madly in love with Betty,
but couldn't pluck up enough
courage to pop the question face to
face. Finally he decided to ask her
on the telephone. "Darling!" he
blurted out, "will you marry me?"
"Of course, I will, you silly boy," she
replied, "who is it speaking?"

What's a cow's favorite love song?
When I Fall In Love, It Will Be For
Heifer.

Bill: My sister has lovely long red
hair all down her back.
Will: Pity it's not on her head!

Hilda: I love cookies!
Tilda: That's because you're
crackers!

Freda: Boys whisper they love me.
Fred: Well, they wouldn't admit it out loud, would they?

What do you call an amorous insect?
The Love Bug.

What did one amorous flea say to the other?
I love you aw-flea.

How did the octopus lovers walk down the road?
Arm in arm in arm in arm in arm in arm in arm in arm.

One worm said to the other, "I love you, I love you, I love you."
"Don't be stupid," the other worm said, "I'm your other end!"

What do snakes write on the bottom of their letters?
With love and hisses.

What do two lovesick owls say
when it's raining?
Too-wet-to-woo!

Friends

"Come see my new kittens," said Laura.

"How cute," said Cindy, watching them play. "Will you have to get your cats a license?"

"Of course not," said Laura. "They don't know how to drive!"

Amy: Did you find your cat?

Karen: Yes, he was in the refrigerator.

Amy: Goodness, is he OK?

Karen: He's more than OK; he's a cool cat.

Penny: Will you join me in a cup of hot chocolate?
Mindy: Yes, but do you think we'll both fit?

What did the croaking frog say to her friend?
I think I've got a person in my throat.

What did the termite say when she saw that her friends had completely eaten a chair?
Wooden you know it!

"Your cat has been staring at that light in the yard," said Kerrie. "Is he all right?"

"Oh," said Misty, "he's trying to make a moth bawl."

Abigail: I won 186 goldfish.
Stacy: Where do you keep them?
Abigail: In the bathroom.
Stacy: What do you do when you want to take a bath?
Abigail: I blindfold them.

What did the mouse say when her
friend broke her front teeth?
Hard cheese.

What did the owl say to her friend
as she flew off?
Owl be seeing you later.

What do you get if King Kong sits
on your best friend?
A flat mate.

Which of the witches' friends eats the fastest?
The goblin.

How does a witch make scrambled eggs?
She holds the pan and gets two friends to make the stove shake with fright.

What do you call a pretty and friendly witch?
A failure.

Why do demons and ghouls get on so well?
Because demons are a ghoul's best friend.

How does a skeleton call her friends? On a telebone.

Did you hear about the witch who turned her friend into an egg?
She kept trying to poach her ideas.

Two cannibals were having their dinner. One said to the other, "I don't like your friend."
The other one replied, "Well put her to one side and just eat the greens."

Two friends were discussing the latest scandalous revelations about a Hollywood actress. "They say she likes her latest husband so much she's decided to keep him for another month," said one to the other.

A girl went to a Halloween party
with a sheet over her head. "Are
you here as a ghost?" asked her
friends.
"No, I'm an unmade bed."
Another girl wore a sheet over her
head. "Are you an unmade bed?"
asked her friends.
"No, I'm an undercover agent,"
she replied.

I enjoy doing my homework.
Even at weekends,
But my best friend's just told me
She thinks I'm round the bend.

My friend is so stupid that she thinks twice before saying nothing.

A stupid girl spent the evening with some friends, but when the time came for her to leave, a terrific storm started with thunder, lightning and torrential rain. "You can't go home in this," said the hostess, "you'd better stay the night."

"That's very kind of you," replied the girl. "I'll just pop home and get my pajamas."

Two beings from outer space landed in Las Vegas and were wandering around the casinos. One of them volunteered to go inside and see what was happening. She came out looking rather shocked. "What's the matter?" asked her friend. "It's a very popular place," replied the first being, "It's full of creatures that keep vomiting up little metal disks."

"My Best Friend, The Witch" – by Ann Otherwitch

My friend is so stupid she thinks that an autograph is a chart showing sales figures for cars.

A monster and a zombie went into a funeral home. "I'd like to order a coffin for a friend of mine who has just died," said the monster. "Certainly ma'am," said the undertaker, "but there was really no need to bring her with you."

Sandra's mother said no young man in his right mind would take her to the school dance in her bikini, so she decided to go with her friend's stupid brother.

Statistics say that one in three people is mentally ill. So check your friends and if two of them seem okay, you're the one.

The young teacher was complaining to her friends about how badly she was being paid. "We get a really poultry amount each month," she said.

"You mean 'paltry'," corrected one of her friends.

"No I don't, I mean 'poultry'," replied the teacher. "What I earn is chicken feed."

Two friends who lived in the city were chatting. "I've just bought a pig," said the first.

"But where will you keep it?" asked the second. "Your yard's much too small for a pig!"

"I'm going to keep it under my bed," replied her friend.

"But what about the smell?"

"He'll soon get used to that."

Cannibal Girl: I've brought a friend home for dinner.

Cannibal Mom: Put her in the fridge and we'll have her tomorrow.

A horrible old witch surprised all her friends by announcing that she was going to get married.

"But," said another old hag, "you always said men were stupid. And you vowed never to marry."

"Yes, I know," said the witch, "but I finally found one who asked me."

Why was the principal not pleased
when she bumped into an old
friend?
They were both driving their cars
at the time.

Jane was telling her friend about
her vacation in Switzerland. Her
friend had never been to
Switzerland, and asked, "What did
you think of the scenery?"
"Oh, I couldn't see much," Jane
admitted. "There were all those
mountains in the way."

Auntie Gladys bought herself a new rear-engine continental car. She took an old friend for a spin, but after only half a mile, the car broke down. Both women got out and opened up the front of the car. "Oh, Gladys," said her friend, "you've lost your engine!"

"Never mind dear," said auntie, "I've got a spare one in the trunk."

Girl to Friend: I'm sorry, I won't be able to come out tonight. I promised Dad that I would stay in and help him with my homework.

Aunt Muriel received a letter one morning, and after reading it burst into floods of tears.

"What's the matter?" asked her friend.

"Oh dear," sobbed Auntie, "It's my favorite nephew. He's got three feet."

"Three feet?" exclaimed her friend. "Surely that's not possible?"

"Well," said Auntie, "his mother's just written to tell me he's grown another foot!"

"Why did you come back early from your vacation?" one of Susie's friends asked her.
"Well, on the first day we were there one of the chickens died and that night we had chicken soup. The next day one of the pigs died and we had pork chops . . ."
"But why did you come back?"
"Well, on the third day the farmer's father-in-law died. What would you have done?"

A friend in need is – someone to avoid!

Girl to Friend: My mum is suffering from a minor neurosis. Every time she sees my school report, she faints.

The proud owner of an impressive new clock was showing it off to a friend. "This clock," he said, "will go for fourteen days without winding."
"Really," replied his friend. "and how long will it go if you do wind it?"

"I hope this plane doesn't travel faster than sound," said the girl to the stewardess.

"Why?"

"Because my friend and I want to talk, that's why."

I thought, Miss Smith, that you wanted yesterday afternoon off because you were seeing your dentist?

That's right, sir.

So how come I saw you coming out of the movie theater with a friend?

That was my dentist.

An old lady coughed violently, and her dentures shot across the room and smashed against the wall. "Oh dear," she said, "whatever shall I do? I can't afford a new set."

"Don't worry," said her friend, "I'll get a pair from my brother for you." The next day the friend came back with the teeth, which fitted perfectly. "This is wonderful," said the old lady. "Your brother must be a very good dentist."

"Oh, he's not a dentist," replied the friend, "he's an undertaker."

Girl to Friend: My dad is so old, when he was at school, history was called current events.

Knock Knock

Knock, knock.
Who's there?
Yule.
Yule who?
Yule never know just how much I
love you.

Knock, knock.
Who's there?
Xena.
Xena who?
Xena minute!

Knock, knock.
Who's there?
Etta.
Etta who?
Etta boy!

Knock, knock.
Who's there?
Kristin.
Kristin who?
Kristining robe.

Knock, knock.
Who's there?
Rena.
Rena who?
Renamok in the shopping mall.

Knock, knock.
Who's there?
Eunice.
Eunice who?
Eunice is like your nephew.

Knock, knock.
Who's there?
Audrey.
Audrey who?
Audrey another drink.

Knock, knock.
Who's there?
Pammy.
Pammy who?
Pammy something nice when you
are at the shops!

Knock, knock.
Who's there?
Cecile.
Cecile who?
Cecile the envelope.

Knock, knock.
Who's there?
Elly.
Elly who?
Ellymentary, my dear Watson.

Knock, knock.
Who's there?
Gertie.
Gertie who?
Gertiesy call!

Knock, knock.
Who's there?
Phoebe.
Phoebe who?
Phoebe way above my price.

Knock, knock.
Who's there?
Grace.
Grace who?
Grace skies are over us.

Knock, knock.
Who's there?
Enid.
Enid who?
Enid some food now.

Knock, knock.
Who's there?
Thea.
Thea who?
Thea later alligator.

Knock, knock.
Who's there?
Olive.
Olive who?
Olive in this house – what are you
doing there?

Knock, knock.
Who's there?
Peg.
Peg who?
Peg your pardon, I've got the wrong door.

Knock, knock.
Who's there?
Dana.
Dana who?
Dana you mind.

Knock, knock.
Who's there?
Aida.
Aida who?
Aida whole sandwich at lunchtime.

Knock, knock.
Who's there?
Cynthia.
Cynthia who?
Cynthia won't listen I'll keep
shouting.

Knock, knock.
Who's there?
Norma.
Norma who?
Normally the butler opens the
door.

Knock, knock.
Who's there?
Marie.
Marie who?
Marie for love.

Knock, knock.
Who's there?
Marietta.
Marietta who?
Marietta whole loaf!

Knock, knock.
Who's there?
Amy.
Amy who?
Amy for the top.

Knock, knock.
Who's there?
Tilly.
Tilly who?
Tilly cows come home.

Knock, knock.
Who's there?
Ruth.
Ruth who?
Ruthless people.

Knock, knock.
Who's there?
Iris.
Iris who?
Iris you would open the door.

Knock, knock.
Who's there?
Cassie.
Cassie who?
Cassie you some time?

Knock, knock.
Who's there?
Willa.
Willa who?
Willa present make you happy?

Knock, knock.
Who's there?
Edna.
Edna who?
Edna clouds.

Knock, knock.
Who's there?
Elizabeth.
Elizabeth who?
Elizabeth of knowledge is a
dangerous thing.

Knock, knock.
Who's there?
Bella.
Bella who?
Bella the ball.

Knock, knock.
Who's there?
Marian.
Marian who?
Mariand her little lamb.

Knock, knock.
Who's there?
Martha.
Martha who?
Martha boys next door are hurting me!

Knock, knock.
Who's there?
Alma.
Alma who?
Almany times do I have to knock?

Knock, knock.
Who's there?
May.
May who?
Maybe it's a friend at the door.

Knock, knock.
Who's there?
Judy.
Judy who?
Judyliver newspapers still?

Knock, knock.
Who's there?
Jade.
Jade who?
Jade a whole pie today.

Knock, knock.
Who's there?
Sophia.
Sophia who?
Sophia nothing . . . fear is
pointless.

Knock, knock.
Who's there?
Denise.
Denise who?
Denise are above the feet.

Knock, knock.
Who's there?
Nancy.
Nancy who?
Nancy a piece of cake?

Knock, knock.
Who's there?
Vanessa.
Vanessa who?
Vanessa time I'll ring the bell.

Knock, knock.
Who's there?
Winnie.
Winnie who?
Winnie is better than losing.

Knock, knock.
Who's there?
Isla.
Isla who?
Isla be seeing you.

Knock, knock.
Who's there?
Samantha.
Samantha who?
Samantha baby have gone for a
walk.

Knock, knock.
Who's there?
Della.
Della who?
Della tell ya that I love ya?

Knock, knock.
Who's there?
Louise.
Louise who?
Louise coming to tea today.

Knock, knock.
Who's there?
Clara.
Clara who?
Clara space on the table.

Knock, knock.
Who's there?
Penny.
Penny who?
Penny for your thoughts.

Knock, knock.
Who's there?
Bridie.
Bridie who?
Bridie light of the silvery moon.

Knock, knock.
Who's there?
Olivia.
Olivia who?
Olivia is great for cooking.

Knock, knock.
Who's there?
Briony.
Briony who?
Briony, beautiful sea.

Knock, knock.
Who's there?
Daryl.
Daryl who?
Daryl be the day.

Graffiti about Girls

Don't do homework. No teacher can blame you for something you haven't done.

My sister can play the piano by ear. I'd rather she went and played it over there!

God made Adam but thought he could do better so he made little girls.

Cinderella married for money. She really put her foot in it!

Black Magic – by Sue Pernatural

My needlework teacher is a sew and sew!

My teacher's got a pretty face if you can read between the lines.

Bo Peep did it for the insurance.

Is she Hungary?
Alaska.
Yes Siam.
I'll Fiji then don't Russia.

My mother had a nervous
breakdown trying to fit round
tomatoes into square sandwiches.

Teacher loves me – she puts
kisses against all my sums.

The optician's daughter keeps making a spectacle of herself.

My sister uses massacre on her eyes.

"Long Walk" by Miss D. Bus

Is an operetta a girl who works for AT&T?

"Sleep" by Annie Stethic

Gorgons had snakes in their hair and looked like women only more horrible.

Why does mom say she's been shopping when she hasn't bought anything?

"In the Country" by Theresa Green

Woman wanted to run up curtains

Sheena is a good dancer.
That's not dancing, someone
spilled coffee in her lap.

I Caught the Loch Ness Monster –
by Janet A. Big-Wun

Girlish
Riddles

What didn't Adam and Eve have
that everyone in the world has
had?
Parents.

Why can't anyone stay angry long
with an actress?
Because she always makes up.

Why was the mother flea so sad?
Because her children were going
to the dogs.

Why did the girl laugh after her operation?
The doctor put her in stitches.

Why do we dress baby girls in pink and baby boys in blue?
Because they can't dress themselves.

What did the burglar say to the lady who caught him stealing her silver?
I'm at your service, ma'am.

What did the girl say when she
opened her piggybank and found
nothing in it?
O I C U R M T

What does every girl have that she
can always count on?
Fingers.

Why did the greedy girl pick all the
white meat off the chicken?
To make a clean breast of it.

When a girl falls into water, what is
the first thing she does?
Gets wet.

What happened when the Eskimo
girl fell out with her boyfriend?
She gave him the cold shoulder.

What did one angel say to the
other angel?
Halo!

What is it a girl looks for but hopes she won't find?
A hole in her pantyhose.

Why is a girl extravagant with her clothes?
When she has a new dress she wears it out the first day.

Why did the girl keep a ruler on her newspaper?
Because she wanted to get the story straight.

If Janet's mother is Mary's daughter, what relation is Janet to Mary?
Mary is Janet's grandmother.

If a woman is born in Italy, grows up in England, goes to America and dies in Baltimore, what is she?
Dead.

What do well-behaved young lambs say to their mothers?
"Thank ewe!"

Why did the girl buy a set of tools?
Everyone said she had a screw
loose.

Why is a bride always out of luck
on her wedding day?
Because she never marries the
best man.

When Adam introduced himself to
Eve, what three words did he use
which read the same backward
and forward?
Madam, I'm Adam.

Why is a lady's belt like a garbage truck?
Because it goes around and around and gathers the waist.

What is the difference between a hungry girl and a greedy girl?
One longs to eat and the other eats too long.

What trees do fortunetellers look at?
Palms.

There was a girl in our town,
Silk an' satin was her gown.
Silk an' satin, gold an' velvet;
Guess her name, three times I've
telled it.
Anne.

What did Cinderella say when her
photos didn't arrive?
"Some day my prints will come."

Why did the Invisible Man's wife understand her husband so well?
Because she could see right through him.

When does a timid girl turn to stone?
When she becomes a little bolder (boulder).

Why didn't the girl go to work in the wool factory?
Because she was too young to dye.

What is the difference between a
soldier and a young lady?
One faces the powder; the other
powders her face.

Why did the girl's granny knit her
three socks for Christmas?
Because she wrote to say she had
grown another foot.

Why did the girl tear the
calendar?
Because she wanted to take a
month off.

What relation is a child to its own
father when it's not its own
father's son?
Daughter.

Why did the girl put her bed in the
fireplace?
So she could sleep like a log.

When is a chair like a woman's
dress?
When it is satin.

Why did the girl sit on her watch?
She wanted to be on time.

What kind of star wears
sunglasses?
A movie star.

Luke had it first, Paul had it last;
boys never have it; girls have it but
once; Miss Polly had it twice in the
same place, but when she married
Peter Jones she never had it
again. What is it?
The letter L.

Why did the girl take a ruler to
bed?
She wanted to see how long she
slept.

Why did the 280-pound girl marry
the 400-pound man?
She wanted a big wedding.

What did Santa Claus's wife say
during a thunderstorm?
"Come and look at the rain, dear."

Why were the girl's snaps not ready when she called for them?
The photographer was a late developer.

Why are good intentions like fainting ladies?
They need carrying out.

There Was a Young Lady From . . .

There was a young lady from Hyde
Who ate some green apples and
died.
The apples fermented
Inside the lamented
And made cider inside her inside.

Our favorite teacher, Miss Rockey,
Wanted to train as a jockey.
But, sad to recall,
She grew far too tall.
So now she teaches us hockey.

There was a young girl from Hyde
Who fell down a hole and died.
 Her unfortunate mother
Tripped up on another
And now they're interred side by
side.

There was a young cannibal from
Kew
Whose girlfriend said "I'll be true,
But please understand
That along with my hand
The rest of me comes with it, too."

A javelin thrower called Vicky
Found the grip of her javelin
sticky.
When it came to the throw
She just couldn't let go –
Making judging the distance
quite tricky.

There was a young lady one fall
Who wore a newspaper dress to a
ball.
The dress caught fire
And burned her entire
Front page, sporting section and
all.

There was a young lady from
Niger,
Who smiled as she rode on a tiger.
They returned from the ride
With the lady inside,
And the smile on the face of the
tiger.

There once was a lady named
Perkins
Who simply doted on gherkins
They were so nice
She ate too much spice
And pickled her internal workins.

There once was a lady named Lynn
Who was so uncommonly thin,
That when she assayed
To drink lemonade,
She slipped through the straw and
fell in!

There once was a man from Great
Britain
Who interrupted two girls at their
knittin'.
Said he with a sigh,
"That park bench, well I
Just painted it right where you're
sittin'."

A pretty young lady called Splatt
Was mistaken one day for a cat
By a man called Van Damm
Who made pets into jam –
And now she's spread out rather
flat.

There was a young maid from
Madras
Who had a magnificent ass;
Not rounded and pink,
As you probably think –
It was grey, had long ears, and ate
grass.

A lady from Florence called Nella
Had a dog that was such a good
smeller
It could sniff out a meal
From as far off as Lille,
And if it was nice it would tell her.

There was a young woman named
Bright
Whose speed was much faster
than light.
She set out one day
In a relative way,
And returned on the previous
night.

A lady musician called Hamp
Was prone to quite severe cramp.
One day at the harp
She got stuck in F-sharp,
And was freed by acetylene lamp.

A charming young singer named
Hannah
Got caught in a flood in Savannah;
As she floated away,
Her sister – they say -
Accompanied her on the piannah!

A nervous young lady called
Hughes
Never knew quite what to choose.
The harder she'd try
The less she knew why,
Or whether, and if so, then whose?

A nervous young woman called Fay
Always used to react with dismay
At a match being struck,
Or the quack of a duck.
"Hello, Fay!" made her faint clean
away.

A man by the name of Geneen
Was asked by his wife where he'd
been.
He Ummed and he Ahhhed –
So she hit him, quite hard,
On the head, with a large soup
tureen.

A chiropodist – friends call her
Dawn –
Used to do people's feet on her
lawn;
But the neighbors complained
When a lady, unnamed,
Was hit in the eye by a corn.

For a student whose name is
Kathleen,
With a mind that's not overly keen,
Graduation is sure,
As she's hardly demure
And has often been seen with the
Dean.

A lady from Louth with a lisp
Liked her sausages specially crisp.
But in trying to say
That she liked them that way
She covered her friends in a
mitht.

A lady from Brighton called Palmer
Became quite an expert snake
charmer.
The snakes called her Miss,
And gave a loud hiss
When it looked as if someone
would harm her.

There was a young lady called Jen,
Who angered her friends now and
then
By running up stairs
And shouting, "Who cares?"
Then doing the whole thing again.

An earnest young lady called
Soames
Wrote a very large book about
gnomes;
But the tales were so tall
And the sales were so small
She was left with huge unwanted
tomes.

A girl from Seattle called Lucy
One day came over all goosy.
Although it seemed strange,
She got used to the change,
And by Christmas was really quite
juicy.

Tongue
Twisters

Blissful Brenda blithely backing Britain.

Doris was dreadfully downhearted and depressed when she discovered how deplorably she was disorientated.

Peggy Pringle's posture at the piano was painful and practically impossible when she practiced on the piccolo.

Lucy lingered, looking longingly for her lost lapdog.

Vera valued the valley violets.

She sat in solitude and isolation sighing and singing sad songs.

Hetty and Harry hurried homeward to hasten from the howling hurricane.

Theresa tried on twenty-three silver thimbles.

Mrs Lister's sister spoke Spanish, Swedish and Swahili and spent a season in the Sudan where she suffered from sunstroke.

The heiress found the heirloom haphazardly hanging from the high shelf.

Dimpled Dinah danced in dainty
dimity down the dunes.

Peggy Babcock, Peggy Babcock,
Peggy Babcock.

As I went into the garden
I saw five brave maids
Sitting on five broad beds
Braiding broad braids.
I said to these five brave maids
Sitting on five broad beds
Braiding broad braids,
"Braid broad braids, brave maids."

Katie quailed after the quarrel at a quarter to one with Queenie and Cleo.

Connie couldn't keep to the cloisters: the cloisters were cloying and claustrophobic.

The duchess danced gracefully and daintily and drew delighted glances.

The lieutenant's lady loved liqueurs and liked to linger late with lots of crème de menthe.

Betty Brown blinked and brandished the broom at the big labrador.

Miranda makes marvelous mince pies that melt in the mouth.

Cut Clara a cauliflower and catch crawling crabs, Caroline.

Claire collected the cabbages, carrots, cauliflower, crumbly cakes and macaroni cheese.

Sally's selfish selling shellfish, So Sally's shellfish seldom sell.

Colin cuddled Connie in the car and caught his camera on the clutch.

Shy Susie Shipton sewed the seams of Sammy's Sunday shirts.

A dozen droopy damsels dawdled despondently down the docks.

A shadow sometimes settled on the settle where Sheila sat her Saluki.

Milly Meacham met a man minding a monkey for a millionaire.

Amanda Millicent McGuire amended a messy manuscript with muddled emendations.

Gladys' glamorous granny grew more and more garrulous.

February found Philippa floundering through the field of thistles.

Florence Freeman fell forward and frightened her father.

Languorous Lottie Lott looked lugubriously at the lowering clouds and longed for lighter nights.

Felicity tried to facilitate the fortunes of the fevered fellow and found him far from thankful.

She sewed shirts seriously.

Gloria Groot glued a groat to Gregory's goat.

The royal lady received the roses regally at the recent reception.

Eleven little laundry-maids locked up in the linen press.

Five fashionable females flying to France for fresh French fashions.

Flora's fan fluttered feebly and her fine fingers fidgeted.

Pretty Polly Perkin polished paper plates and plaster plaques.

Sly Susie said sleepwalking was
solely the somnambulist's concern.

Mr Hadden had on his new
Homburg hat but Mrs Hadden
hadn't a hat and after adding her
money which was inadequate she
had to adapt her old hat.

Fanny Fetter found a fan
A fan found Fanny Fetter,
But Fanny Fetter lost her fan
– And wept till she felt better.

I was looking back
To see if she was looking back
To see if I was looking back
To see if she was looking back at
me.

She was a thistle-sifter
And she sifted thistles.
She had a sieveful of sifted
thistles,
And a sieveful of unsifted thistles.
The sieveful of unsifted thistles
She had to sift
She was a thistle-sifter.

Susan Schumann shot a solitary
chamois and received a short,
sharp salutary shock from such a
shameless slaughter.

A maid with a duster
Made a furious bluster
Dusting a bust in the hall.
When the bust it was dusted
The bust it was busted,
The bust it was dust, that's all.

Fancy Nancy didn't fancy doing
fancy work.

But Fancy Nancy's fancy aunty did fancy
fancy
Fancy Nancy doing fancy work!

Sarah saw a sash shop full of showy, shiny sashes.

Lily's lovely lolly cost a lot of Lily's lovely lolly.

Grace's gray-green gloves glided gracefully to the ground.

Wheedling, weeping Winnie wails wildly.

She stops at the shops where I shop,
And if she shops at the shop where I shop
I won't stop at the shop where she shops!

Sooty Sukey shook some soot from sister Suzie's sooty shoes.

Crazy Clara catches crawling crabs.

Once I heard a mother utter,
"Daughter, go and shut the shutter."
"Shutter's shut," the daughter uttered,
"I can't shut it any shutter."

Can Kitty cuddle Clara's kitten?

Sunshine Susie shone her shoes
with soap and shoe-shine.

Gay Gladys glanced bravely at
grave Greta and glided glitteringly
past guilty Grace at the glorious
garden gala.

Dorothy dawdled and doodled in a
daydream as she dusted down
the dresser in the drawing room.

Three fluffy feathers fell from feeble Phoebe's fan.

Lottie licks lollies lolling in the lobby.

She chews cream cheese and fresh cress sandwiches.

Shirley slid the scissors down the slippery slanting slates.

Though a kiss be amiss,
She who misses the kisses,
As Miss without kiss,
May miss being Mrs!

Beautiful Bonnie Bliss blows
blissfully beautiful bubbles.

Susan shineth shoes and socks,
Socks and shoes shineth Susan,
She ceaseth shining shoes and
socks,
For socks and shoes shock Susan.

Lisbeth lisps lengthy lessons.

Shy Sam Smith thought Sarah
Short so sweet.

Sheila's Shetland pony shied,
Shooting Sheila on the shore.
Shaking Sheila, stupefied,
Struggled homeward, stiff and
sore.

Freckle-faced Florence.

Thelma saw thistles in the thick
thatch.

Which is the witch that wished the
wicked wish?

Rita relishes Russian radishes.

I saw Esau kissing Kate.
I saw Esau, he saw me.
And she saw I saw Esau.

Our great-grand-gran is a greater
great-grand-gran than your
great-grand-gran is.

Shy sly Sheila sat shivering in her
slim, shiny, shot-silk smock.

Betty Batter had some butter,
"But," she said, "this butter's
bitter.
If I bake this bitter butter,
It will make my batter bitter."

The savor of the silly scent the
sentry sent to Millicent.

With a shovel Sarah slowly shifted
sifted cinders.